STEP IN

Engaging math activities, games, and
fact cards **PLUS** fun math-related stories
to reinforce key math concepts!

Senior Editor: Janet Sweet
Design/Production: Rebekah Lewis
Art Director: Moonhee Pak
Managing Editor: Stacey Faulkner

Table of Contents

MATH Introduction

Understanding math is vitally important to your child's success in school and in life. The MATH series by Creative Teaching Press is expertly developed to help young children understand math concepts and ideas that relate to their world. Appealing activities and games, along with stories, fact cards, and a helpful glossary, support math success while making math fun.

Positive attitudes about math at home—including yours as a parent—lay the foundation for math success in school. Make a point of helping your child notice math-related activities and concepts that occur in his or her daily world, such as pointing out house numbers or counting cars or noticing clothing sizes. Also encourage your child to try these activities to practice thinking mathematically:

- Sort—clothes, toys
- Measure—ingredients, sizes
- Estimate—distance, time
- Tell—where, when, and how
- Play—card and board games
- Count—stairs, grocery items
- Compare—shapes, sizes, numbers
- Pretend—to be a waiter, cashier

Helping your child experience fun, real-world math interaction at an early age will build math enjoyment, knowledge, and success throughout your child's life.

MATH Glossary

Learning math can be a challenge for young children. At a time when they are just learning to recognize and understand basic words and language skills, young learners must also figure out the symbols, concepts, and specialized vocabulary of math—all of which can seem like an entirely different language.

Specifically designed for Kindergartners and First Graders, this MATH Glossary provides visual examples with clear, easy-to-understand definitions for the important math terms they must learn.

For extra support, these words appear in red font both here and in the math-related story questions. Calling out math words in this way helps young learners understand that math is a meaningful part of everyday language and does not exist solely on math worksheets.

SYMBOLS AND CONCEPTS

+	addition sign (also called *plus sign*)
−	subtraction sign (also called *minus sign*)
=	equal sign
$	dollar sign
¢	cent sign

LOCATION AND POSITION WORDS

after	16 17	17 is after 16
before	7 8	7 is before 8
between	23, 24, 25	24 is between 23 and 25
first	first	
last	last	
next	next	
over		The frog jumps over the log.
under		There is water under the bridge.

MATH⁺ Step In • Gr. K–1 © 2011 Creative Teaching Press

COUNTING, SHAPE, AND MATH-FACT WORDS

add

combine numbers or objects together

$3 + 2 = 5$

less than

smaller than

1 is less than 6

compare

look at objects to learn how they are the same and different

more than

bigger than or larger

5 is more than 2

count back

Start at 10 and count back 2 spaces.

$10 - 2 = 8$

number line

Use the number line to count.

count on

Start at 8 and count on 2 spaces.

$8 + 2 = 10$

shapes

circle   rectangle   square   triangle

diamond   heart   oval   star

difference

$9 - 3 = 6$ ← difference

subtract

take away objects from a group

$5 - 3 = 2$

estimate

find out <u>about</u> how many or how much

The crayon is about 4 paper clips long.

sum

$4 + 1 = 5$ ← sum

graphs

Favorite Color

blue
red
0 1 2 3 4 5 6 7 8

bar graph

Favorite Fruits

apples
bananas
grapes

picture graph

tally

use tally marks to count

half

tens

2 tens = 20

TIME, MONEY, AND MEASUREMENT WORDS

clock		minute hand	
days of the week	Sunday Monday Tuesday Wednesday Thursday Friday Saturday	months of the year	January February March April May June July August September October November December
dime	10¢ or 10 cents = 10 pennies	nickel	5¢ or 5 cents = 5 pennies
dollar	$1.00 or one dollar = 100 pennies	o'clock	on the hour = three o'clock
half dollar	50¢ or 50 cents = 50 pennies	__ thirty	30 minutes after the hour = three thirty
hour hand		penny	1¢ or 1 cent
inch	0 1 2 3 4 5	quarter	25¢ or 25 cents = 25 pennies
length	how long something is	size	small medium large

MATH+ Step In • Gr. K–1 © 2011 Creative Teaching Press

If the Shoe Fits

Draw a line to match the sock and the shoe that shows the same number.

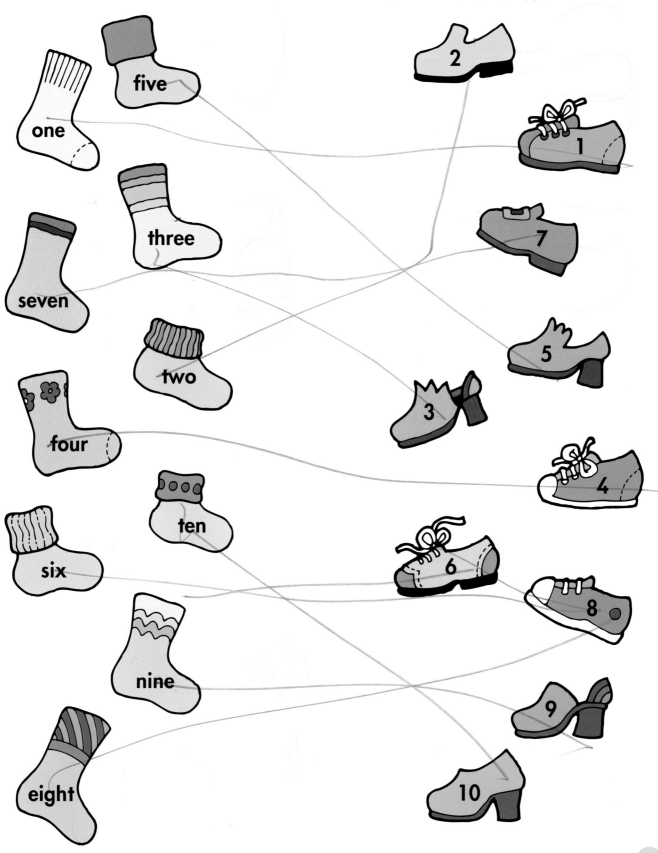

Star Bright–Moonlight

⚙ Circle sets of two. Write the number of sets in each box.

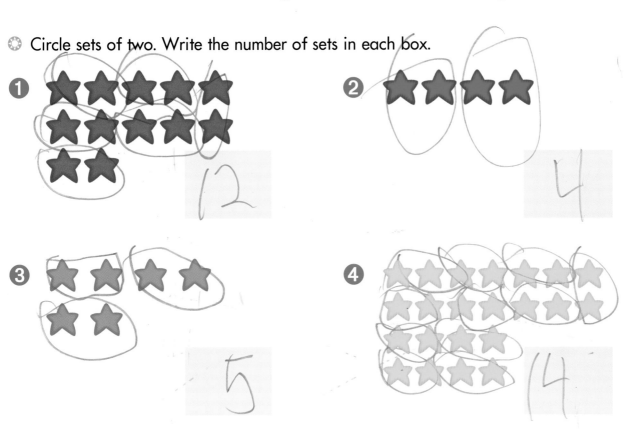

1 12

2 4

3 5

4 14

⚙ Circle sets of five. Write the number of sets in each box.

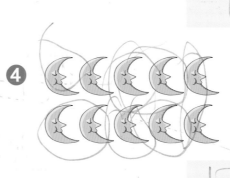

1

2 4

3

4 10

MATH+ Step In • Gr. K–1 © 2011 Creative Teaching Press

Tally Ho!

Count and write the number of tally marks.

1

10

2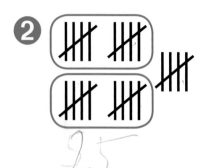

25

3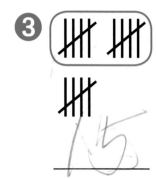

15

4

16

5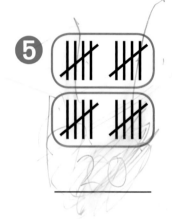

20

6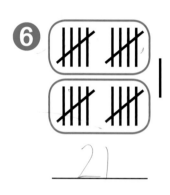

21

7

12

8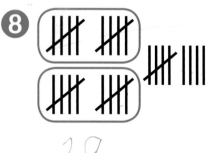

29

9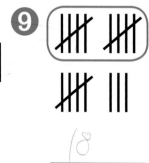

18

10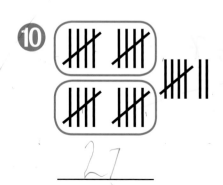

27

11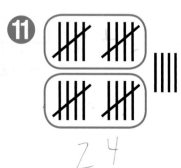

24

12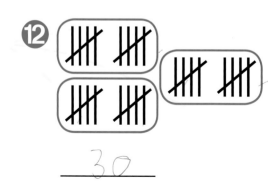

30

An Icy Path

Help the penguin get to his friends.

Add and find the sums on the numbered spaces.

Color those spaces to make a path.

1   2 + 2 = ___4___

2   10 + 2 = ___12___

3   22 + 2 = ___24___

4   12 + 2 = ___14___

5   36 + 2 = ___38___

6   24 + 2 = ___26___

7   18 + 2 = ___20___

MATH⁺ Step In • Gr. K–1 © 2011 Creative Teaching Press

Order That Number

Write the number that comes **before**, **between**, or **after**.

1 _____, 11, 12   **2** 41, 42, _____   **3** 18, 19, _____

4 22, _____, 24   **5** 14, _____, 16   **6** _____, 31, 32

7 _____, 37, 38   **8** 48, 49, _____   **9** 2, 3, _____

10 _____, 40, 41

Write the number word for the missing number.

11 eleven, _____, thirteen

12 eighteen, nineteen, _____

13 fourteen, fifteen, _____

Caterpillar, Caterpillar

✿ Write the number for each number word.

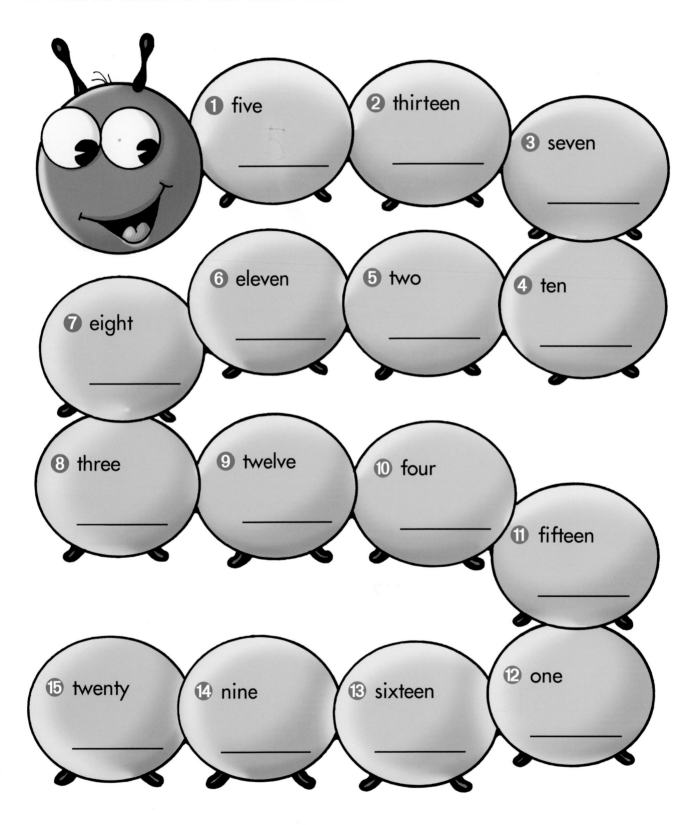

1. five _____
2. thirteen _____
3. seven _____
4. ten _____
5. two _____
6. eleven _____
7. eight _____
8. three _____
9. twelve _____
10. four _____
11. fifteen _____
12. one _____
13. sixteen _____
14. nine _____
15. twenty _____

MATH+ Step In • Gr. K–1 © 2011 Creative Teaching Press

Leap Frog

☼ Use the number line to add.

1 8 + 2 = __10__

2
$$
\begin{array}{r}
7 \\
+1 \\
\hline
8
\end{array}
$$

3
$$
\begin{array}{r}
3 \\
+7 \\
\hline
10
\end{array}
$$

4 4 + 4 = __8__

☼ Use the number line to count back.

5 10 − 5 = __5__

6 10 − 2 = __8__

7 7 − 1 = __6__

8
$$
\begin{array}{r}
5 \\
-3 \\
\hline
2
\end{array}
$$

Count by 5s

❀ Write the missing numbers to help the bee find the hive.

MATH+ Step In • Gr. K–1 © 2011 Creative Teaching Press

All in Order

⚙ Look at the order.

⚙ Follow the directions.

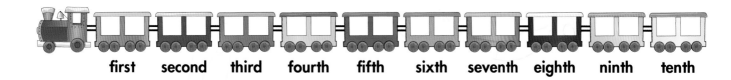

first   second   third   fourth   fifth   sixth   seventh   eighth   ninth   tenth

1 Circle the first. Underline the third.

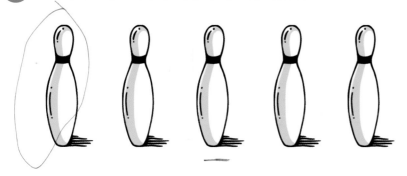

2 Circle the fourth. Underline the fifth.

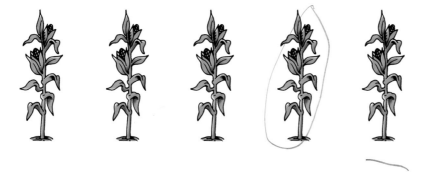

3 Circle the second. Underline the third.

Counting by 2s

○ Count by 2s.

○ Write the number that comes next.

1 2, 4, ___6___   **2** 18, 20, ___22___

3 12, 14, ___16___   **4** 10, 12, ___14___

5 20, 22, ___24___   **6** 14, 16, ___18___

7 26, 28, ___30___   **8** 28, 30, ___32___

9 0, 2, ___4___   **10** 34, 36, ___38___

MATH+ Step In • Gr. K–1 © 2011 Creative Teaching Press

Bird's Path to 10

❀ Help the bird fly to its nest.

❀ Begin at the number under "Start."

❀ Find the path of numbers that add up to 10. End at the number above "End."

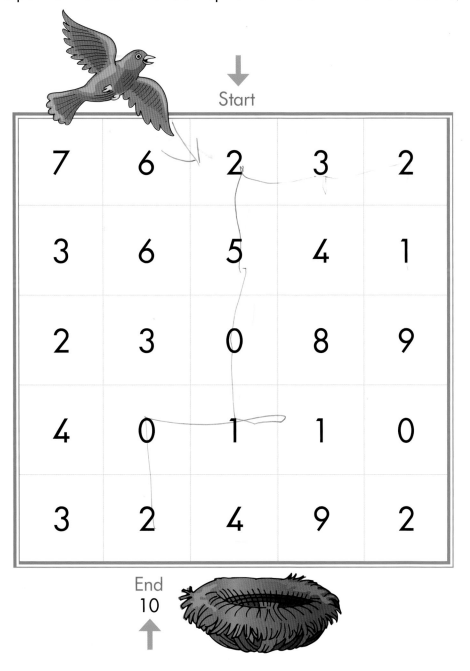

Start

7	6	2	3	2
3	6	5	4	1
2	3	0	8	9
4	0	1	1	0
3	2	4	9	2

End
10

The path of numbers that add up to 10 is:

_____.

Addition Math Maze

- Follow the math maze from "Start" to "End."
- Solve the addition problems as you go.
- Write the final sum in the starburst.

MATH+ Step In • Gr. K–1 © 2011 Creative Teaching Press

Number Scramble

- Choose two numbers in each group to make addition facts.

- Cross out the two numbers in each group that you did not use.

- The first one is done for you.

12 ~~7~~ 8 ~~11~~	**④ 8 6 ⑨**
_8_ + _12_ = 20	_9_ + _4_ = 13
_12_ + _8_ = 20	_4_ + _9_ = 13

3 11 7 9

____ + ____ = 16

____ + ____ = 16

7 9 9 12

____ + ____ = 18

____ + ____ = 18

6 9 8 3

____ + ____ = 14

____ + ____ = 14

13 6 5 12

____ + ____ = 19

____ + ____ = 19

9 12 8 6

____ + ____ = 15

____ + ____ = 15

11 9 5 8

____ + ____ = 17

____ + ____ = 17

13 12 5 7

____ + ____ = 20

____ + ____ = 20

Line It Up

- Draw lines connecting three numbers to make addition facts.
- Start in the far left column, and use the pictures as clues.
- Write each addition fact on the lines.
- The first one is done for you.

6 + ___1___ = ___7___

2 + ___3___ = ___5___

0 + ___4___ = ___4___

3 + ___4___ = ___7___

1 + ___7___ = ___8___

5 + _____ = _____

MATH+ Step In • Gr. K–1 © 2011 Creative Teaching Press

Fun on the Farm

- ⚙ Add.
- ⚙ Then write the sums in the boxes under the problems.
- ⚙ Match the sums to the letters to find the answer to the riddle.

3	4	5	6	7
R	M	E	V	O

Riddle: What did the grumpy cow say to the haystack?

1 + 3	3 + 4	6 + 1
4	7	7

2 + 4	3 + 2
6	5

5 + 2	3 + 3	4 + 1	2 + 1
7	6	5	3

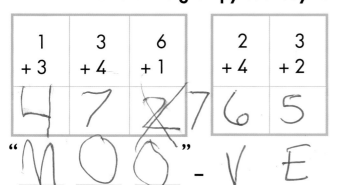

"M O O"- V E   O V E R

0	1	2	3	4	5	6	7
G	O	E	B	N	R	I	H

Riddle: What did the horse say when he moved into the barn?

4 + 3	5 + 1

2 + 2	1 + 1	4 + 2	0 + 0	3 + 4

1 + 2	0 + 1	0 + 5

"___ ___   ___ ___ ___ ___ ___"

___ ___   ___ ___ ___

Magic Trick

✿ Find the magic number. The clues will help you.

✿ Cross out a number on the hat as you read each clue.

✿ The number that is left is the magic number.

1 It is not 5 + 1

2 It is not 12 – 7

3 It is not 3 + 1

4 It is not 3 + 9

5 It is not 10 – 8

6 It is not 6 + 2

7 It is not 15 – 12

8 It is not 7 + 4

The magic number is _____!

MATH+ Step In • Gr. K–1 © 2011 Creative Teaching Press

Number Riddles

- ☼ Solve the number riddle.
- ☼ Circle the correct answer.

1 I have 4 tens and 3 ones. What number am I?

34   43   42

2 I have 6 tens and 0 ones. What number am I?

6   600   60

3 I have 5 ones and 1 ten. What number am I?

63   15   35

4 I have 3 tens and 3 ones. What number am I?

3   33   30

5 I have 2 ones and 6 tens. What number am I?

26   62   20

6 I have 3 tens and 7 ones. What number am I?

37   33   73

7 I have 9 ones and 0 tens. What number am I?

99   90   9

8 I have 1 ten and 7 ones. What number am I?

11   17   18

Shape Find

⚙ Find the hidden shapes.

⚙ Circle them.

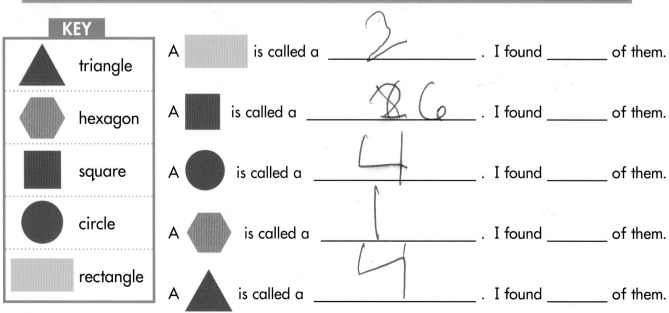

KEY	
▲	triangle
⬡	hexagon
■	square
●	circle
▭	rectangle

A ▭ is called a ___2___ . I found _____ of them.

A ■ is called a ___8 6___ . I found _____ of them.

A ● is called a ___4___ . I found _____ of them.

A ⬡ is called a ___4___ . I found _____ of them.

A ▲ is called a ___4___ . I found _____ of them.

MATH+ Step In • Gr. K–1 © 2011 Creative Teaching Press

What Size Is It?

⚙ Draw a line under the biggest hat.

⚙ Circle the smallest hat.

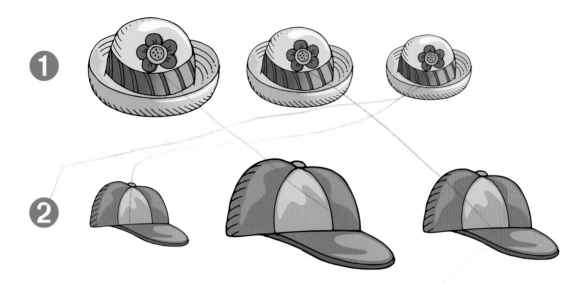

1

2

⚙ Write **1** under the biggest.

⚙ Write **2** under the medium size.

⚙ Write **3** under the smallest.

3

4

Find the Months

- Find and circle the names of the months.
- Answers will appear across, forward and backward, down, and diagonally.

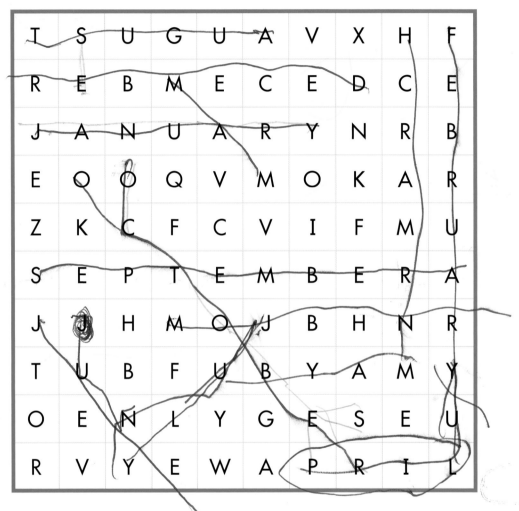

T	S	U	G	U	A	V	X	H	F
R	E	B	M	E	C	E	D	C	E
J	A	N	U	A	R	Y	N	R	B
E	O	O	Q	V	M	O	K	A	R
Z	K	C	F	C	V	I	F	M	U
S	E	P	T	E	M	B	E	R	A
J	J	H	M	O	J	B	H	N	R
T	U	B	F	U	B	Y	A	M	Y
O	E	N	L	Y	G	E	S	E	U
R	V	Y	E	W	A	P	R	I	L

JANUARY   JULY

FEBRUARY   AUGUST

MARCH   SEPTEMBER

APRIL   OCTOBER

MAY   NOVEMBER

JUNE   DECEMBER

MATH+ Step In • Gr. K–1 © 2011 Creative Teaching Press

Guess How Long

- About how long would each activity take?
- Circle your answer.

walk to school

(minutes)   days   months

build a building

~~minutes~~   days   (months)

play a game

(minutes)   days   months

drive across the country

minutes   (days)   months

spend a day at school

(minutes)   hours   days

grow a plant

~~minutes~~   hours   (days)

It's About Time!

⚙ Circle the objects that answer the questions.

Which one tells you the date?

Which one tells you the time of day?

- -

⚙ Draw hands on the clocks to match the time.

9:00

3:00

- -

⚙ What will the time be an hour after?

One hour after, it will be

 12 : 9

One hour after, it will be

_____ : _____

- -

⚙ What will the time be two hours after?

Two hours after, it will be

 12 : 11

⚙ What was the time an hour before?

One hour before, it was

_____ : _____

28

Heads or Tails?

⚙ Identify each coin. Write **penny**, **nickel**, **dime**, **quarter**, or **half dollar** and its value.

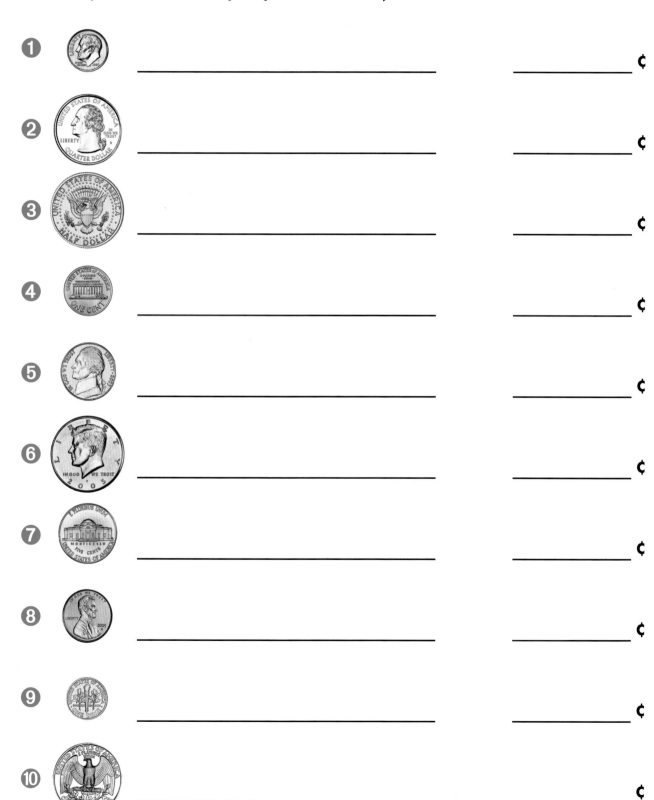

1 _____ _____ ¢

2 _____ _____ ¢

3 _____ _____ ¢

4 _____ _____ ¢

5 _____ _____ ¢

6 _____ _____ ¢

7 _____ _____ ¢

8 _____ _____ ¢

9 _____ _____ ¢

10 _____ _____ ¢

Even Amounts

- Help the bee get to its hive.
- Write the value of the coins in each box.
- Then circle the boxes that have even amounts to find the bee's path.

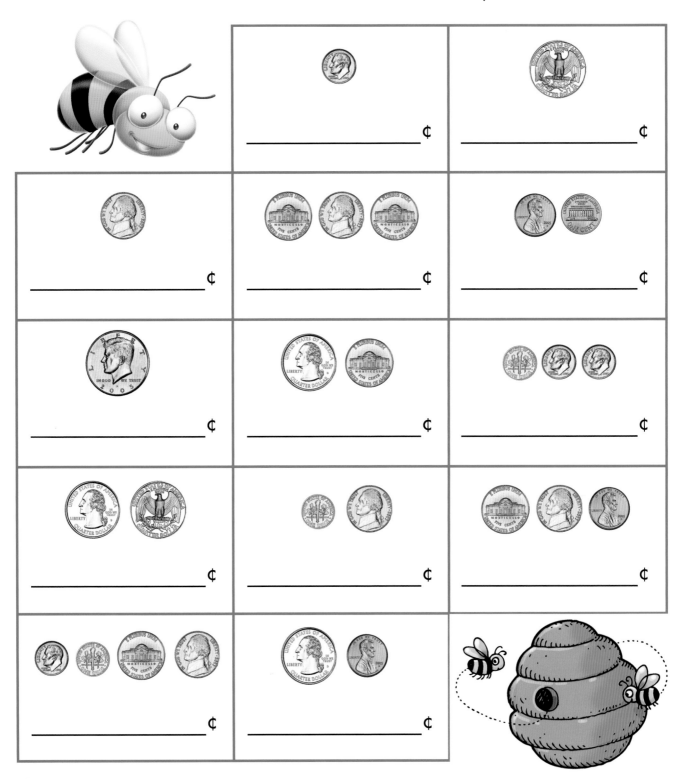

MATH+ Step In • Gr. K–1 © 2011 Creative Teaching Press

Do I Have Enough?

Write **yes** or **no** for each question.

1 Bob has .

Is it enough to buy this?

 25¢

_____

2 Sue has .

Is it enough to buy this?

 15¢

_____

3 Teri has   .

Is it enough to buy this?

 50¢

_____

4 Frank has .

Is it enough to buy this?

 30¢

_____

5 Mike has .

Is it enough to buy this?

 40¢

_____

6 Lauren has .

Is it enough to buy this?

 45¢

_____

What Equals a Dollar?

1 How many [penny] equal a dollar? _____

2 How many [nickel] equal a dollar? _____

3 How many [dime] equal a dollar? _____

4 How many [quarter] equal a dollar? _____

5 How many [half dollar] equal a dollar? _____

6 In each box, draw a different combination of coins that equal a dollar.

MATH+ Step In • Gr. K–1 © 2011 Creative Teaching Press

How Much?

⊛ Circle the object that is heavier.

 1

⊛ Circle the object that is lighter.

 3

⊛ Circle the object that holds more.

 5

⊛ Circle the object that holds less.

 7

How Long?

⚙ Circle the object that is longer.

1 　　　**2**

⚙ Circle the object that is shorter.

3 　　　**4**

⚙ How many inches long is each object?

5 The crayon is _____ inches long.　　

6 The marker is _____ inches long.　　

⚙ Circle how long each activity lasted.

7  from `10:00` to `10:30`

　　a. 1 hour
　　b. ½ hour

8  from  to

　　a. 1 hour
　　b. ½ hour

⚙ Circle the object that shows a longer amount of time.

9

MATH+ Step In • Gr. K–1 © 2011 Creative Teaching Press

Build a Zoo

✿ Cut out the zoo pictures at the bottom.

✿ Follow the directions in the KEY below to paste the pictures in the right places.

	1	2	3	4	5	6
A						
B						
C						
D						
E						
F						

KEY

1. Place the parking lot in C-1.
2. Place the lion exhibit in C-6.
3. Place the camel exhibit in D-4.
4. Place the zoo entrance in E-2.
5. Place the monkey exhibit in A-3.
6. Place the bear exhibit in F-3.
7. Place the snack stand in E-5.
8. Place the reptile exhibit in B-4.

zoo entrance | bear exhibit
camel exhibit | parking lot
snack stand | monkey exhibit
lion exhibit | reptile exhibit

Crack the Code

- Use the code to solve the riddle.
- Write a letter for each picture symbol. The first one has been done for you.

A	C	E	I	K	P	S	T	U
✳	✪	◆	✳	✚	♥	★	❀	☀

Riddle: You can't drink from this cup. What is it?

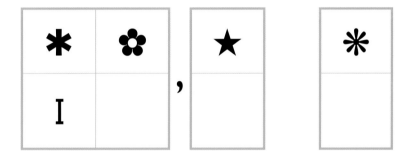

I T , S A

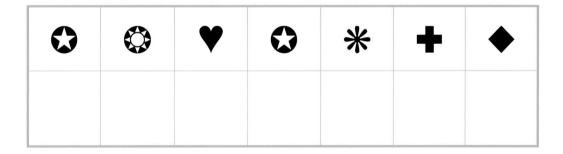

C U P C A K E

Cat and Dog: The Super Snack

⚙ Is Cat eating from the 1st cup, the 3rd cup, or the 5th cup?

Cat and Dog wanted a snack.

✿ Who is sitting in the bigger seat, Cat or Dog?

Cat had a cup of raisins.
Dog had a cup of peanuts.

✺ What shape is on Cat's cup?

✺ What shape is on Dog's cup?

They poured in their cups,
and they mixed it all up.

⚙ What is the sum of adding 1 cup plus
1 cup?

⚙ What math symbol do you use
for adding?

MATH+ Step In • Gr. K–1 © 2011 Creative Teaching Press

**It was better than before,
but they wanted something more.**

☼ Do you think this story will be about
adding or subtracting?

☼ What word in the story sentence helps
explain your answer?

They called Mouse.

☼ How many more animals are there than telephones?

MATH+ Step In • Gr. K–1 © 2011 Creative Teaching Press

Mouse came over with a cup of pretzels.

✺ What is 1 more than 2?

He poured in his cup,
and they mixed it all up.

✺ What's another way of writing
1 + 1 + 1?

**It was better than before,
but they wanted something more.**

☼ Look closely at the picture.

☼ If you added the number of animals to the number of cups, what would the sum be?

They called Kitten.

⚙ Count the number of animals in the 1st picture and in the 2nd picture.

⚙ If you added them together, how would you write that as a math fact?

MATH+ Step In • Gr. K–1 © 2011 Creative Teaching Press

Kitten came over with a cup of crackers.

✺ Kitten's cup has circle shapes on it.

✺ Name something else in the picture that has the same shape.

She poured in her cup,
and they mixed it all up.

It was better than before,
but they wanted something more.

How many different things have been added to the snack now?

MATH+ Step In • Gr. K–1 © 2011 Creative Teaching Press

They called Pup.

⚙ What is 1 more than 4?

⚙ What is 3 more than 4?

Pup came over with a cup of chocolate candies.

⚙ Who is standing between Cat and Dog?

⚙ Who is standing between Dog and Mouse?

MATH+ Step In • Gr. K–1 © 2011 Creative Teaching Press

He poured in his cup,
and they mixed it all up.

It was better than before,
and they didn't need any more.

☼ Now how many cups have been added to the snack mix?

☼ If you subtracted the peanuts and the raisins, how many different snack items would there be?

**Then, they all dipped in a cup,
and they split it all up.**

**It was better than before,
and they all got something more!**

⚙ How are Mouse's cup, Cat's cup, and Pup's cup all the same?

⚙ How are they all different?

MATH+ Step In • Gr. K–1 © 2011 Creative Teaching Press

Snacks in Order

✪ Write the ordinal number for each number word.

✪ Draw a line from each ordinal number to its matching story picture.

Word Box

1st	**2**nd	**3**rd	**4**th
first	second	third	fourth

first _____ •   •

second _____ •   •

third _____ •   •

fourth _____ •   •

What Goes Together?

✪ Write a letter in each box to answer each question.

I added chocolate candies. Who am I? ☐

I added pretzels. Who am I? ☐

I added raisins. Who am I? ☐

I added crackers. Who am I? ☐

MATH+ Step In • Gr. K–1 © 2011 Creative Teaching Press

Let's Measure It!

✺ What do you see here that can help the cat measure?

The fish in the bowl is one inch long.

✿ The line under the fish shows an inch.

✿ What measuring tool would also show an inch?

MATH+ Step In • Gr. K–1 © 2011 Creative Teaching Press

What else is one inch?
Let's measure.

✺ Find the dinosaurs that have about the same line length as the fish.

✺ How many are there?

The fish in the pail is two inches long.

✿ What number word tells you how long the fish is?

What else is two inches?
Let's measure.

✪ How many things on this page are about 2 inches long?

✪ Name them.

The fish in the aquarium is three inches long.

☼ Compare the fish's length to the length of the feeding sign.

☼ Which one is longer?

MATH+ Step In • Gr. K–1 © 2011 Creative Teaching Press

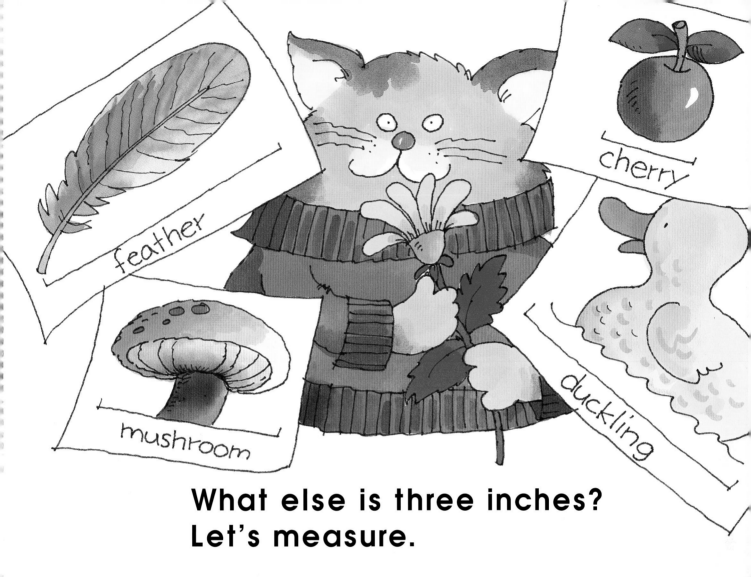

What else is three inches?
Let's measure.

✿ How many things on this page are about 3 inches long?

✿ Name them.

The fish in the river is four inches long.

☼ What is 1 less than 4?

☼ What is 2 more than 4?

MATH+ Step In • Gr. K–1 © 2011 Creative Teaching Press

What else is four inches? Let's measure.

❂ How many things on this page are about 4 inches long?

❂ Name them.

The fish in the lake is five inches long.

✹ Compare this fish to the fish on page 64.

✹ What is the difference in their lengths?

MATH+ Step In • Gr. K–1 © 2011 Creative Teaching Press

What else is five inches?

☼ Name the 2 shortest objects.

The fish in the ocean is six inches long.

✿ How long is half of 6 inches?

MATH+ Step In • Gr. K–1 © 2011 Creative Teaching Press

What else is six inches?

☼ Compare the length of these 3 objects.

☼ Which of these objects is probably longer than 6 inches?

Let's measure everything!

☼ When could it be important to measure a fish?

MATH+ Step In • Gr. K–1 © 2011 Creative Teaching Press

feather

☼ Why would you want to know how long a tent is?

Can you measure a friend?

✸ What do you think the cat will do with the stick?

✸ Do you think the dinosaur is longer or shorter than 7 inches?

MATH+ Step In • Gr. K–1 © 2011 Creative Teaching Press

Where Are the Fish?

⚙ Write where each fish is in each box below.

⚙ Then number the places from smallest to biggest, 1 to 4.

Word Box

| pail | lake | river | fish bowl |

fish bowl

Let's Measure!

✦ Use a ruler to measure what you see under the sea.

[ ] inches

[ ] inches

[ ] inches

[ ] inches

[ ] inch

MATH+ Step In • Gr. K–1 © 2011 Creative Teaching Press

Cat and Dog Make the Best, Biggest, Most Wonderful Cheese Sandwich

- ☸ Compare the size of the objects.
- ☸ Which is bigger, the tomato slice or the pickle slice?

Let's make a cheese sandwich.
First, take a slice of bread.
Next, put some cheese on it.

✸ What is the 2nd step for making the sandwich?

MATH⁺ Step In • Gr. K–1 © 2011 Creative Teaching Press

Then, put another slice of bread on top.

☼ What ingredient did they use 2 times to make the sandwich?

No, no, no!
Let's make a big cheese sandwich.

First, take a big slice of bread.
Next, put a big slice of cheese on it.

☼ Compare the size of the cheese packets.

☼ Which is bigger, the cheese in Cat's hand or the cheese by Cat's chair?

MATH+ Step In • Gr. K–1 © 2011 Creative Teaching Press

Then, put another slice of bread on top.

**No, no, no!
Let's make a bigger cheese sandwich.**

☼ Compare this sandwich to the one on page 77.

☼ How are they the same, and how are they different?

First, take a bigger slice of bread.
Next, put a bigger slice of cheese on it.

✿ Where is the biggest bag of bread?

MATH+ Step In • Gr. K–1 © 2011 Creative Teaching Press

Then, put another slice of bread on top.

No, no, no!
Let's make the biggest cheese sandwich.

⚙ Which would take more time, eating
a big sandwich or eating a bigger
sandwich?

⚙ Explain.

First, take the biggest slice of bread.
Next, put the biggest slice of cheese on it.

✷ What is the 3rd step for making the cheese sandwich?

MATH⁺ Step In • Gr. K–1 © 2011 Creative Teaching Press

Then, put another slice of bread on top.

No, no, no!
Let's make a good, big cheese sandwich.

⚙ Compare this sandwich to the sandwich on page 81.

⚙ How are they the same and how are they different now?

First, take the biggest slice of bread.
Next, put the biggest slice of cheese on it.
Then, put some red tomato on it.

⚙ What is the 3rd step for making the sandwich now?

MATH+ Step In • Gr. K–1 © 2011 Creative Teaching Press

Then, put another slice of bread on top.

No, no, no!
Let's make a better, bigger cheese sandwich.

☼ Compare this sandwich to the sandwich on page 77.

☼ What is the difference in the number of steps it takes to make them?

First, take the biggest slice of bread.
Next, put the biggest slice of cheese on it.

Then, put some red tomato on it.
Then, put some green pickles on it.

✿ Count the bags of bread, and then count the tomato slices.

✿ Which has more?

MATH+ Step In • Gr. K–1 © 2011 Creative Teaching Press

Then, put another slice of bread on top.

No, no, no!
Let's make the best, biggest cheese sandwich.

☼ Which is bigger, the sandwich or
Dog's face?

First, take the biggest slice of bread.
Next, put the biggest slice of cheese on it.
Then, put some red tomato on it.

Then, put some green pickles on it.
Then, put some crisp lettuce on it.
Then, put another slice of bread on top.

❂ What is the 5th step for making the sandwich now?

❂ Tell what happens in the step before that.

MATH+ Step In • Gr. K–1 © 2011 Creative Teaching Press

No, no, no!
Let's make the best, biggest,
most wonderful cheese sandwich.

☼ How is this sandwich bigger than the
sandwich on page 87?

Let's cut it in half and share it!

✸ Which is bigger, half of the sandwich above or the sandwich on page 89?

✸ Now compare the half sandwich above to the sandwich on page 77 and tell which is bigger.

MATH+ Step In • Gr. K–1 © 2011 Creative Teaching Press

Make a Strip Book

- Write your name on the first page.
- Cut along the solid lines and staple.
- Read your book.

The Biggest, Best Sandwich

by

1

First, I take a slice of bread.

2

Next, I add a slice of cheese.

3

Then, I add tomato and pickles.

4

Last, I add lettuce and a slice of bread.
Yum!

5

Time of Day Card Game

❶ Cut apart the cards below.

❷ Put them in the correct order from morning to night.

Rat Race Game

① Cut apart the Addition Fact Cards on pages 107, 109, 111, 113, and 115. Mix them up and set them facedown.

② **Player A and Player B:** Take turns drawing a card, adding the numbers, and following the directions on the game board. If your answer is:

- 13–16, move ahead 2 spaces.

- 9–12, move ahead 1 space.

- 4–8, move back 1 space.

M A T E R I A L S
✓ game cards
   (see directions above)
✓ game markers
✓ game board (page 96)

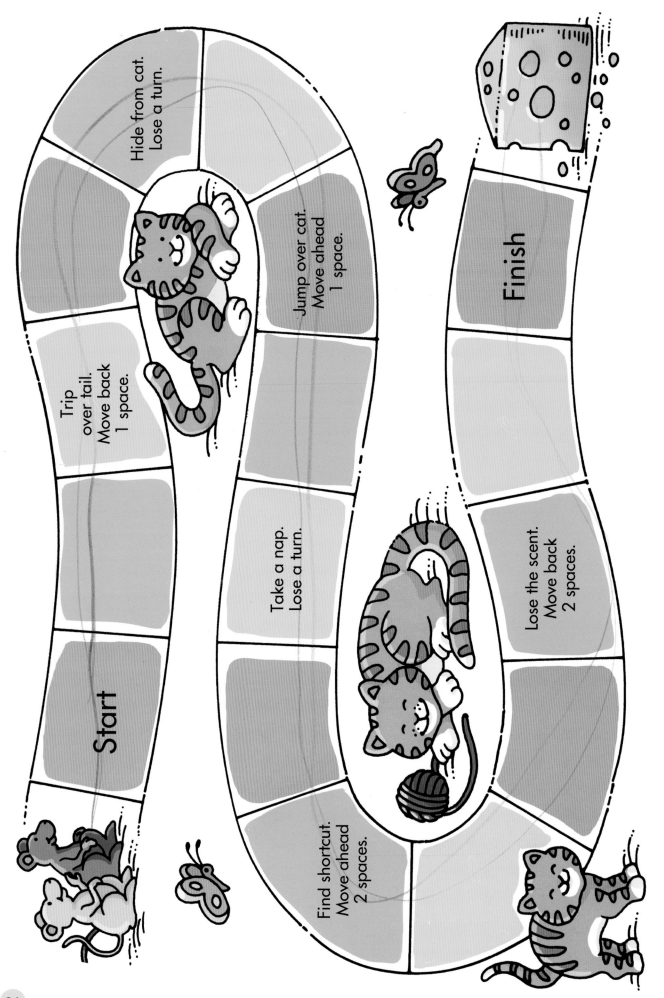

Start

Trip over tail. Move back 1 space.

Hide from cat. Lose a turn.

Jump over cat. Move ahead 1 space.

Take a nap. Lose a turn.

Find shortcut. Move ahead 2 spaces.

Lose the scent. Move back 2 spaces.

Finish

Winter Wonderland Game

HOW TO PLAY

1. Cut apart the picture squares on the bottom half of the page.
2. Match and paste each numbered picture square to its corresponding box below.

MATERIALS
✓ scissors
✓ glue

1, 2, _____	IIII I	6, _____, 8	IIII IIII I
twelve	13, 14, _____	16, _____, 18	IIII IIII IIII IIII
5, 10, 15, _____	10, 20, _____	thirty-five	one hundred

All-Around Fun Game

HOW TO PLAY

1. Cut out the squares. Place the square with the face in the center of the table. Place the rest of the squares faceup where players can see them.

2. **Player A:** Choose a square with an addition problem or a sum that correctly matches the card with the face.

3. **Player B:** Choose a square that matches another addition problem to its sum.

4. Take turns adding squares until all the combined squares form a shape.

5. What shape did they make? _____

MATERIALS
- ✓ scissors
- ✓ game squares (pages 99 and 101)

11

7 + 8

16

7 + 7

9 + 7

12

9 + 9

15

All-Around Fun Game

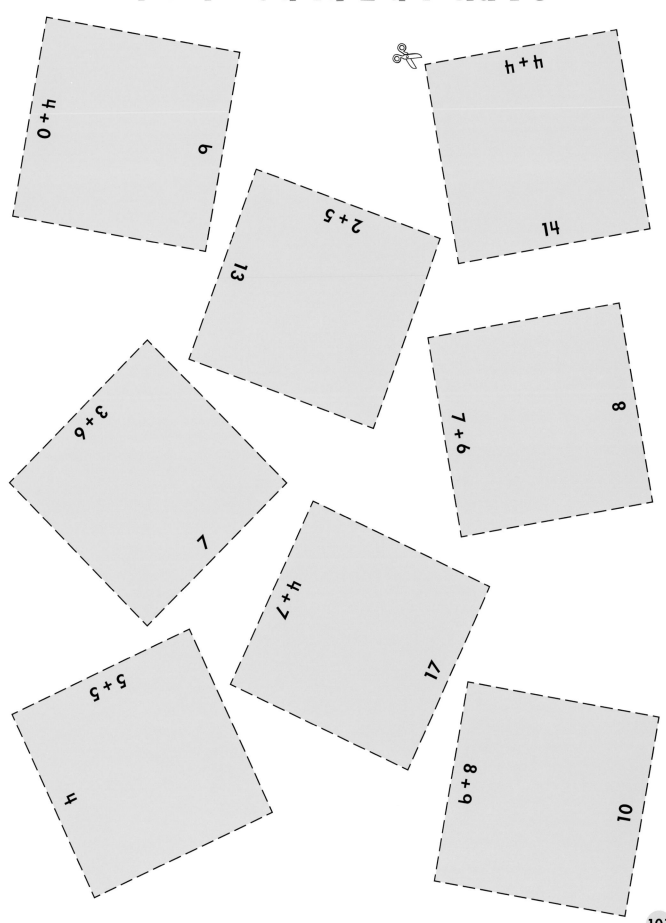

4 + 0

9

4 + 4

14

2 + 5

13

7 + 6

8

3 + 6

7

4 + 7

17

5 + 5

4

8 + 9

10

MATH+ Fact Cards

Tips for Using MATH+ Fact Cards

Before cutting the fact cards apart, consider laminating them in order to use them with a dry-erase marker. Laminating the cards also makes them more durable. Punching a hole in the upper left-hand corner of each card and storing the cards on a ring is also a good way to keep the cards organized and easy to use.

Here are some suggestions for using the fact cards:

- Use a timer to see how quickly each math fact is recognized. Begin with a small number of cards. Add more cards once your child achieves increased speed and confidence.

- Challenge your child to restate the math fact in another way. For example, 11:30 can be restated as half past eleven.

- Have your child identify the complete fact family for a particular equation. For example, 2 + 3 = 5 is part of the following fact family: 3 + 2 = 5, 5 − 3 = 2, and 5 − 2 = 3.

- Play a sorting game. Have your child sort the answers to the addition fact cards on pages 107, 109, 111, 113, and 115 into groups of even and odd numbers. Another option is to shuffle the addition fact cards and sort their answers into groups of 1–10 and 11–20.

The Properties of Zero (0)

When adding zero to a number, the number stays the same.

1 + 0 = 1	2 + 0 = 2
3 + 0 = 3	4 + 0 = 4
5 + 0 = 5	6 + 0 = 6
7 + 0 = 7	8 + 0 = 8
9 + 0 = 9	10 + 0 = 10

When subtracting zero from a number, the number stays the same.

1 – 0 = 1	2 – 0 = 2
3 – 0 = 3	4 – 0 = 4
5 – 0 = 5	6 – 0 = 6
7 – 0 = 7	8 – 0 = 8
9 – 0 = 9	10 – 0 = 10

When subtracting a number from itself, the answer is zero.

1 – 1 = 0	2 – 2 = 0
3 – 3 = 0	4 – 4 = 0
5 – 5 = 0	6 – 6 = 0
7 – 7 = 0	8 – 8 = 0
9 – 9 = 0	10 – 10 = 0

MATH+ Facts When Adding by 1

1 + 1 = 2	2 + 1 = 3
3 + 1 = 4	4 + 1 = 5
5 + 1 = 6	6 + 1 = 7
7 + 1 = 8	8 + 1 = 9
9 + 1 = 10	10 + 1 = 11

MATH+ Facts When Subtracting by 1

10 – 1 = 9	9 – 1 = 8
8 – 1 = 7	7 – 1 = 6
6 – 1 = 5	5 – 1 = 4
4 – 1 = 3	3 – 1 = 2
2 – 1 = 1	

MATH+ Step In • Gr. K–1 © 2011 Creative Teaching Press

Number and Number Word Fact Cards

one	two
three	four
five	six
seven	eight
nine	ten

Number and Number Word Fact Cards

2 ‖	1 ∣
4 ‖‖	3 ‖‖
6 卌 ∣	5 卌
8 卌 ‖‖	7 卌 ‖
10 卌 卌	9 卌 ‖‖

Addition Fact Cards

$2 + 2 = 4$

$2 + 3 = 5$

$2 + 4 =$

$2 + 5 = 8$

$2 + 6 = 8$

$2 + 7 =$

$2 + 8 = e$

$2 + 9 =$

$2 + 10 =$

$3 + 3 = 6$

Addition Fact Cards

5	4
7	6
9	8
11	10
6	12

MATH+ Step In • Gr. K–1 © 2011 Creative Teaching Press

Addition Fact Cards

$3 + 4 =$

$3 + 5 =$

$3 + 6 =$

$3 + 7 =$

$3 + 8 =$

$3 + 9 =$

$3 + 10 =$

$4 + 4 =$

$4 + 5 =$

$4 + 6 =$

Addition Fact Cards

8	7
10	9
12	11
8	13
10	9

MATH+ Step In • Gr. K–1 © 2011 Creative Teaching Press

Addition Fact Cards

4 + 7 =	4 + 8 =
4 + 9 =	4 + 10 =
5 + 5 =	5 + 6 =
5 + 7 =	5 + 8 =
5 + 9 =	5 + 10 =

Addition Fact Cards

12	11
14	13
11	10
13	12
15	14

MATH+ Step In • Gr. K–1 © 2011 Creative Teaching Press

Addition Fact Cards

$6 + 6 =$

$6 + 7 =$

$6 + 8 =$

$6 + 9 =$

$6 + 10 =$

$7 + 7 =$

$7 + 8 =$

$7 + 9 =$

$7 + 10 =$

$8 + 8 =$

Addition Fact Cards

13	12
15	14
14	16
16	15
16	17

MATH+ Step In • Gr. K–1 © 2011 Creative Teaching Press

Addition and Size Fact Cards

8 + 9 =	8 + 10 =
9 + 9 =	9 + 10 =
10 + 10 =	more, less
small, medium, large	big, bigger, biggest
long, longer, longest	short, shorter, shortest

Addition and Size Fact Cards

18	17
19	18
more less	20
big bigger biggest	small medium large
short shorter shortest	long longer longest

MATH+ Step In • Gr. K–1 © 2011 Creative Teaching Press

Ordinal Number Fact Cards

first	second
third	fourth
fifth	sixth
seventh	eighth
ninth	tenth

MATH+ Step In • Gr. K–1 © 2010 Creative Teaching Press

Ordinal Number Fact Cards

2nd	1st
4th	3rd
6th	5th
8th	7th
10th	9th

MATH+ Step In • Gr. K–1 © 2011 Creative Teaching Press

Time Fact Cards

Sunday	Monday	Tuesday	January	February	March
Wednesday	Thursday	Friday	April	May	June
Saturday			July	August	September
			October	November	December

_____ o'clock

_____ o'clock

_____ o'clock

_____ o'clock

_____ thirty

_____ thirty

_____ thirty

_____ thirty

Time Fact Cards

Months of the Year	Days of the Week
3 o'clock 3:00	12 o'clock 12:00
9 o'clock 9:00	6 o'clock 6:00
three thirty 3:30	twelve thirty 12:30
nine thirty 9:30	six thirty 6:30

MATH+ Step In • Gr. K–1 © 2011 Creative Teaching Press

Money Fact Cards

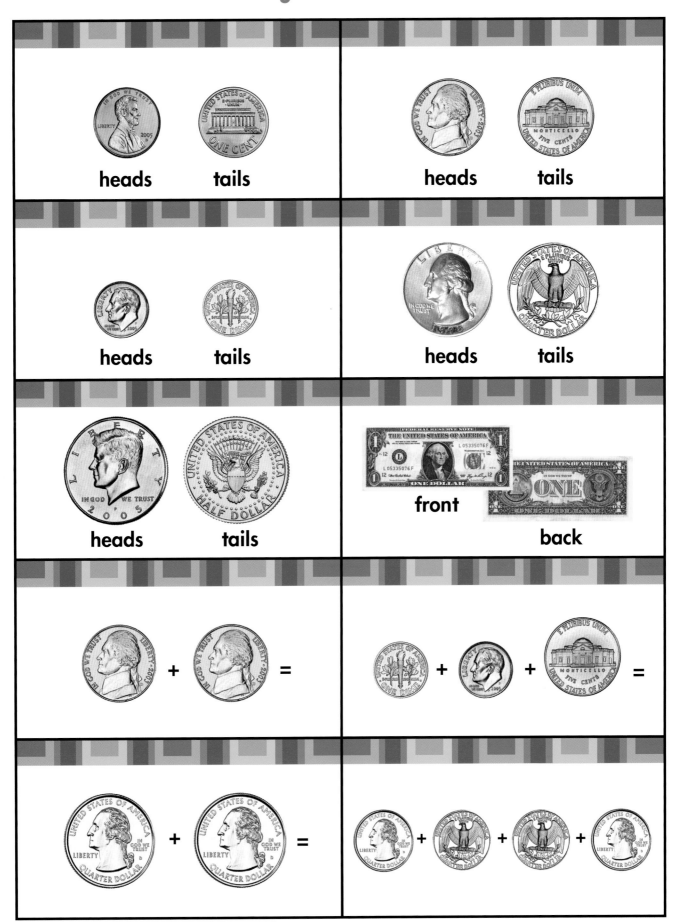

heads   tails   heads   tails

heads   tails   heads   tails

heads   tails   front   back

Money Fact Cards

5¢ a nickel	1¢ a penny
25¢ a quarter	10¢ a dime
$1.00 a dollar	50¢ a half-dollar
25¢	10¢
$1.00	50¢

MATH+ Step In • Gr. K–1 © 2011 Creative Teaching Press

Answer Key

PAGE 7

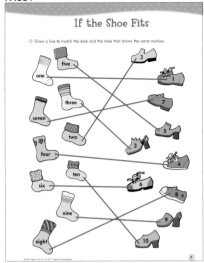

If the Shoe Fits

PAGE 8
1. 6
2. 2
3. 3
4. 11
1. 3
2. 1
3. 5
4. 2

PAGE 9
1. 10
2. 25
3. 15
4. 16
5. 20
6. 21
7. 12
8. 29
9. 18
10. 27
11. 24
12. 30

PAGE 10

An Icy Path

❶ 2 + 2 = 4
❷ 10 + 2 = 12
❸ 22 + 2 = 24
❹ 12 + 2 = 14
❺ 36 + 2 = 38
❻ 24 + 2 = 26
❼ 18 + 2 = 20

PAGE 11
1. 10
2. 43
3. 20
4. 23
5. 15

6. 30
7. 36
8. 50
9. 4
10. 39
11. twelve
12. twenty
13. sixteen

PAGE 12
1. 5
2. 13
3. 7
4. 10
5. 2
6. 11
7. 8
8. 3
9. 12
10. 4
11. 15
12. 1
13. 16
14. 9
15. 20

PAGE 13
1. 10
2. 8
3. 10
4. 8
5. 5
6. 8
7. 6
8. 2

PAGE 14
10, 20, 25, 40, 45, 55, 65, 75, 80, 85, 90, 100

PAGE 15

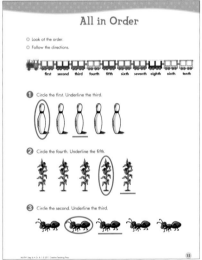

All in Order

PAGE 16
1. 6
2. 22
3. 16
4. 14
5. 24
6. 18
7. 30
8. 32
9. 4
10. 38

PAGE 17

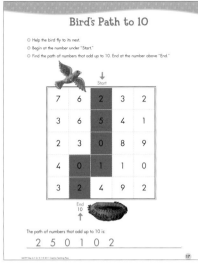

Bird's Path to 10

The path of numbers that add up to 10 is:

2 5 0 1 0 2

PAGE 18

Addition Math Maze

PAGE 19

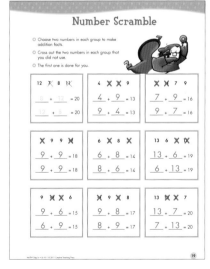

Number Scramble

12 8	4 9	7 9
8 + = 20	4 + 9 = 13	7 + 9 = 16
12 + = 20	9 + 4 = 13	9 + 7 = 16

9 9	6 8	13 6
9 + 9 = 18	6 + 8 = 14	13 + 6 = 19
9 + 9 = 18	8 + 6 = 14	6 + 13 = 19

9 6	9 8	13 7
9 + 6 = 15	9 + 8 = 17	13 + 7 = 20
6 + 9 = 15	8 + 9 = 17	7 + 13 = 20

PAGE 20

Line It Up

- Draw lines connecting three numbers to make addition facts.
- Start in the far left column, and use the pictures as clues.
- Write each addition fact on the lines.
- The first one is done for you.

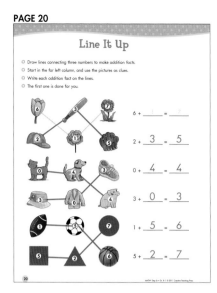

6 + 1 = 7

2 + 3 = 5

0 + 4 = 4

3 + 0 = 3

1 + 5 = 6

5 + 2 = 7

PAGE 24

Shape Find

- Find the hidden shapes.
- Circle them.

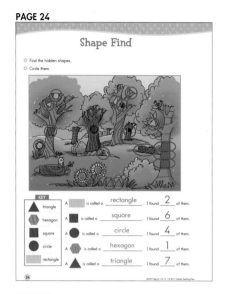

KEY

triangle	A ▭ is called a	rectangle	I found 2 of them.
hexagon	A ◼ is called a	square	I found 6 of them.
square	A ● is called a	circle	I found 4 of them.
circle	A ⬡ is called a	hexagon	I found 1 of them.
rectangle	A ▲ is called a	triangle	I found 7 of them.

PAGE 28

It's About Time!

- Circle the objects that answer the questions.

Which one tells you the date?   Which one tells you the time of day?

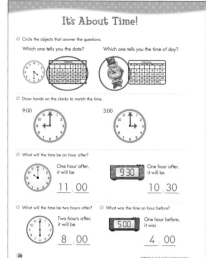

- Draw hands on the clocks to match the time.

9:00   3:00

- What will the time be an hour after?

One hour after, it will be **11:00**

One hour after, it will be **10:30**

- What will the time be two hours after?   What was the time an hour before?

Two hours after, it will be **8:00**

One hour before, it was **4:00**

PAGE 21

Fun on the Farm

- Add.
- Then write the sums in the boxes under the problems.
- Match the sums to the letters to find the answer to the riddle.

3	4	5	6	7
R	M	E	V	O

Riddle: What did the grumpy cow say to the haystack?

1 +3	3 +4	6 +1		5 +2	3 +3	4 +1	2 +1
4	7	7		6	5	7	6 3

"M O O"- V E   O V E R

0	1	2	3	4	5	6	7
G	O	E	B	N	R	I	H

Riddle: What did the horse say when he moved into the barn?

4 +3	5 +1		2 +2	1 +1	4 +2	0 +0	3 +4		3 +0	1 +0	0 +5
7	6		4	2	6	0	7		3	1	5

H I   N E I G H - B O R

PAGE 22

The magic number is 7!

PAGE 23

1. 43
2. 60
3. 15
4. 33
5. 62
6. 37
7. 9
8. 17

PAGE 25

What Size Is It?

- Draw a line under the biggest hat.
- Circle the smallest hat.

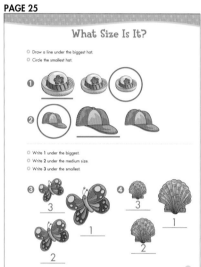

1

2

- Write 1 under the biggest.
- Write 2 under the medium size.
- Write 3 under the smallest.

3   3   4   3

3   1

1

2

PAGE 26

Find the Months

- Find and circle the names of the months.
- Answers will appear across, forward and backward, down, and diagonally.

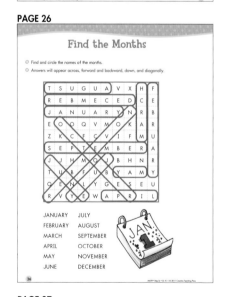

JANUARY	JULY
FEBRUARY	AUGUST
MARCH	SEPTEMBER
APRIL	OCTOBER
MAY	NOVEMBER
JUNE	DECEMBER

PAGE 27

Walk to school—minutes
Build a building—months
Play a game—minutes
Drive across the country—days
Spend a day at school—hours
Grow a plant—days

PAGE 29

1. dime; 10¢
2. quarter; 25¢
3. half dollar; 50¢
4. penny; 1¢
5. nickel; 5¢
6. half dollar; 50¢
7. nickel; 5¢
8. penny; 1¢
9. dime; 10¢
10. quarter; 25¢

PAGE 30

Even Amounts

- Help the bee get to its hive.
- Write the value of the coins in each box.
- Then circle the boxes that have even amounts to find the bee's path.

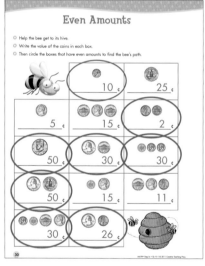

10¢	25¢
5¢	15¢	2¢
50¢	30¢	30¢
50¢	15¢	11¢
30¢	26¢

PAGE 31

1. no
2. yes
3. no
4. yes
5. no
6. yes

PAGE 32

1. 100
2. 20
3. 10
4. 4
5. 2
6. Drawings will vary but should total a dollar.

PAGE 33
1. the book
2. the tiger
3. the slice of cake
4. the penny
5. the bus
6. the kettle
7. the spoon
8. the cup

PAGE 34
1. the bus
2. the celery stalk
3. the square
4. the smaller pencil
5. The crayon is 5 inches long.
6. The marker is 7 inches long.
7. b
8. a
9. the April calendar

PAGE 35

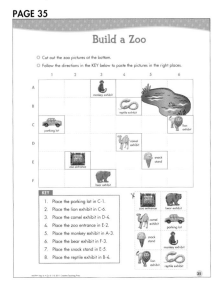

PAGE 37
Riddle Answer: IT'S A CUPCAKE

PAGE 39
The 1st cup

PAGE 40
Dog

PAGE 41
Cat's cup has the star shape on it.
Dog's cup has the square shape on it.

PAGE 42
2 cups
+

PAGE 43
Adding
The word **more**

PAGE 44
1

PAGE 45
3

PAGE 46
Possible answers: 3; 1 + 2; 2 + 1

PAGE 47
6

PAGE 48
3 + 1 = 4

PAGE 49
Kitten's eyes

PAGE 50
4

PAGE 51
5
7

PAGE 52
Pup
Kitten

PAGE 53
5
3

PAGE 54
They have the same colors.
They have different shapes (or designs) on them.

PAGE 55

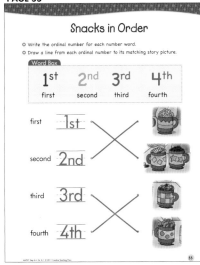

PAGE 56

PAGE 57
The cubes (or blocks)

PAGE 58
Possible answers: A ruler, a measuring stick, a measuring tape, a yardstick

PAGE 59
3

PAGE 60
two

PAGE 61
3
The airplane, the bus, and the truck

PAGE 62
The feeding sign

PAGE 63
2
The feather and the duckling

PAGE 64
3
6

PAGE 65
2
The wagon and the baseball bat

PAGE 66
1 inch

PAGE 67
The cooking pot and the Band Aids

PAGE 68
3 inches

PAGE 69
The line of cubes

PAGE 70
Answers will vary.

PAGE 71
Answers will vary.

PAGE 72
Use it to measure
Longer than 7 inches

PAGE 73

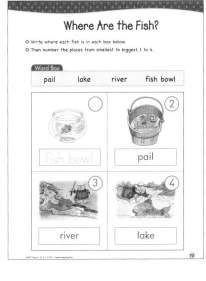

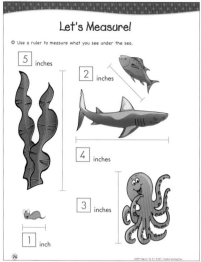

PAGE 75
The tomato slice

PAGE 76
Adding cheese

PAGE 77
Possible answer: They used the bread twice.

PAGE 78
The cheese in Cat's hand

PAGE 79
They have the same ingredients (bread and cheese), but the sandwich on page 77 is smaller.

PAGE 80
On top of Dog's shoulder

PAGE 81
Eating a bigger sandwich
Answers will vary.

PAGE 82
Adding another slice of bread

PAGE 83
They both have bread and cheese, but the sandwich on page 81 is smaller.

PAGE 84
Adding the tomato

PAGE 85
1

PAGE 86
The tomato slices

PAGE 87
The sandwich

PAGE 88
Adding lettuce
Adding pickles

PAGE 89
Possible answers: It has more in it (lettuce); It's taller.

PAGE 90
The sandwich on page 89
The half sandwich above

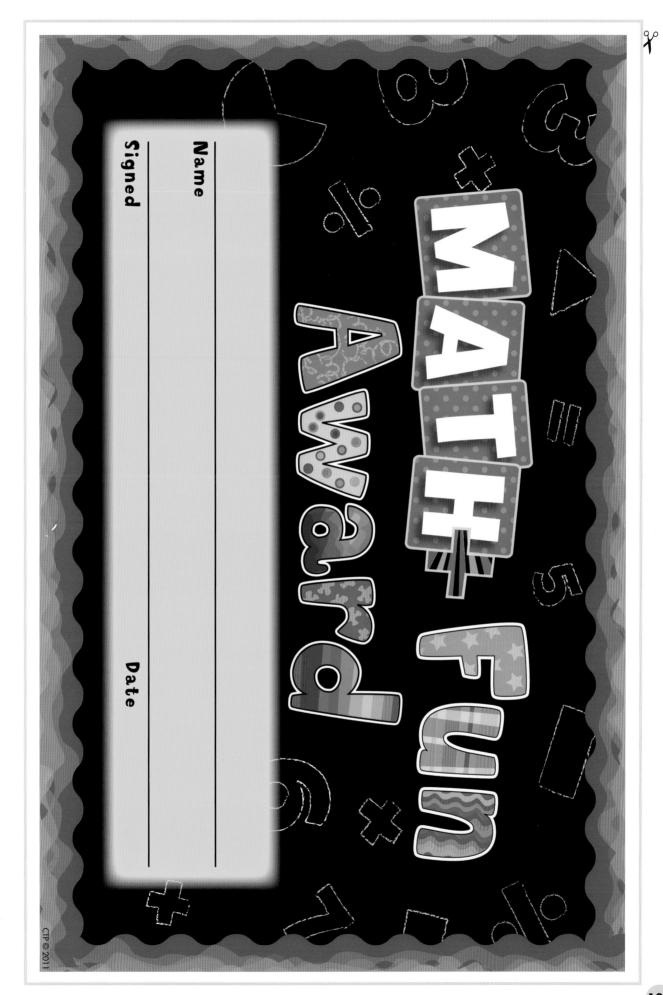

MATH FUN Award

Name _____

Signed _____ Date _____